The Three Neighbors

Yohannes Abraha

copyright © 2024
ATTA, LLC. All rights reserved.

Every day, a human, Benin, would notice a fox named Fox sneaking around his livestock, which included donkeys, goats, sheep, and cows. It was like a game of cat and mouse, with Benin trying to protect his animals from the cunning Fox.

Both Benin and Fox knew that Fox would not dare try to eat the cows because they were too big. However, the goats and sheep were where Fox's eyes shone the brightest they were the perfect size for him, and their meat was delicious. Fox was a handsome creature, and he knew it.

He strutted around with an air of confidence, and the other animals could not help but admire him. His charm and sly nature convinced them he was harmless and friendly until the moment he jumped on his unsuspecting prey.

Fox liked the attention he received from his fellow foxes as well as the admiration from the other animals around him.

Fox hunted alone in the daytime. His charm and quickness made it possible for him to operate in broad daylight.

There was a hyena named Buru who was jealous of Fox because Buru was not as charming, quick, stealthy, or much else like Fox, for that matter. Buru was odd and unfriendly.

Other animals were afraid of him. He did not hunt in the daytime but in the dark hours of the night. He also hunted, mainly as part of a clan.

He rarely hunted alone because he understood that, since other animals feared him, they would not let him get close enough to attack them. Buru hid in a cave all day long, along with his hyena friends and family. He came out at night to hunt when his prey could not easily see him.

Buru was sometimes so hungry because of his night hunting that he would become weak and lose weight. He would easily get tired when he hunted if he had not eaten in a long time. Buru thought to himself, "I bet Fox does not go hungry like I do."

Benin feared Buru as much as Fox, if not more when it came to Benin's livestock. Buru usually hunted as a member of a clan, and he was bigger than Fox. Therefore, Buru could hunt any of Benin's livestock.

This was worrying for Benin, so he had to be careful and count all his livestock every day and make sure they were all in the barn at night. He securely locked up the barn so that Buru and his friends did not eat Benin's animals at night.

One day, when Benin was putting all his animals in the barn, he thought he counted all of them. However, he forgot one lamb that was stranded a distance away from the rest. Benin did not hear its faint bleating. It was still light out, but barely. As the evening slowly set in, it was just bright enough for Fox to still be on the prowl.

Buru did not come out until it was dark, but on this particular day, Buru was feeling very hungry and started looking for food a little earlier than his normal time.

Both Fox and Buru spotted the little lamb, fragile and alone. They both thought that they would be very full going to sleep that night, as their dinner was a few feet away from them. They both salivated at the mouth, thinking of the delicious, tasty dinner they were looking at.

What neither one of them had figured out was that they were both competing for the same meal. Fox was faster and wittier, but Buru was bigger and had one of the strongest jaws of any animal. Fox began to slowly weave his way toward the lamb, using the grass around him to stay hidden.

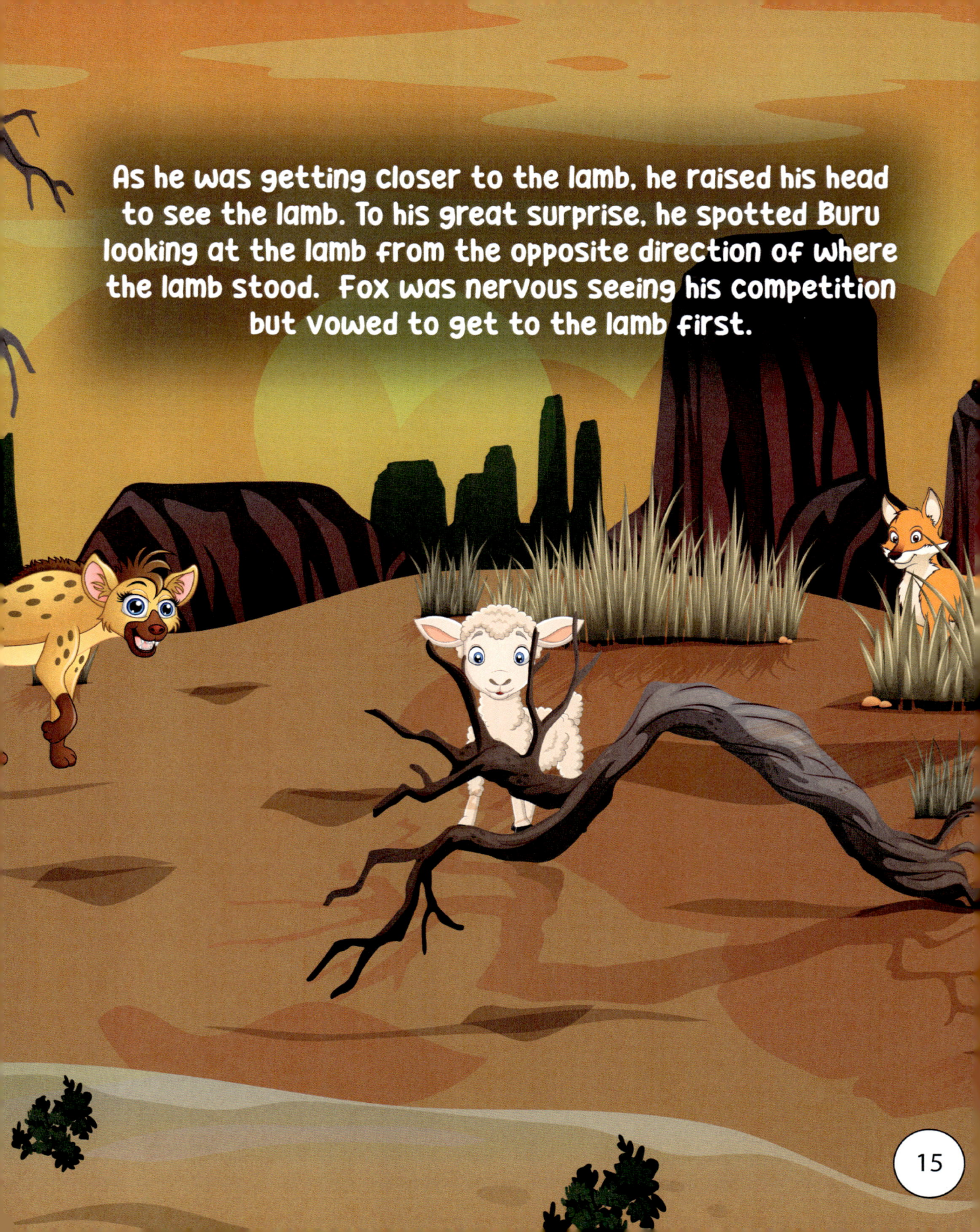

As he was getting closer to the lamb, he raised his head to see the lamb. To his great surprise, he spotted Buru looking at the lamb from the opposite direction of where the lamb stood. Fox was nervous seeing his competition but vowed to get to the lamb first.

Fox saw no other option than to risk the chance that he had to come face to face with Buru because he was too hungry to give up. Although he feared Buru, he could not go another night without eating. It was a risk worth taking, as Fox believed.

Buru saw his delicious dinner as well. Though it was a bit earlier than usual to be looking for food, he could not pass up the opportunity in front of him. He needed food, and he was going to go for it.

He started moving toward the lamb while carefully looking around for any bigger animals or humans. It looked safe, but little did he know that Fox was also carefully making his way toward the lamb.

In the meantime, the lamb's mother was bleating from the barn. Benin became increasingly suspicious as to why this sheep was bleating so much on this day. He said to himself,

"I counted all of the animals, and there were no predators anywhere around."

He had many animals in the barn, so he did not know which of his many sheep was making a fuss. He, however, believed there was something wrong. He once again looked for any predators around his barn, yet there were none. But something caught the corner of his eye as he was checking out his surroundings. He saw a movement of some kind.

He quickly turned around toward where the movement was, and he saw Buru cautiously and purposefully walk. Benin was aware of the difference between aimless wondering and hunting movements of the many predatory animals that lived around him. Benin took a moment to study Buru's careful, targeted walk.

Benin could already tell that Buru was either going to fight another animal to protect his turf or he was going to hunt for food. As Benin studied the event unfolding before him, he was starting to put it together the bleating sheep and Buru's motion. Benin slowly started walking in the same direction as Buru.

Benin would normally avoid going in the same direction as Buru, but Buru was alone, which was less threatening for a big human than if Buru were with his clan. Benin could certainly defend himself against one hyena. As Benin continued to walk slowly, he could hear the low sounding bleat of the lamb. So he started walking a bit faster toward the sound.

He was not sprinting to not attract Buru's attention. Fox, with his speed, got to the lamb first and took a big jump to grab the lamb with his teeth. Suddenly Buru caught Fox with Buru's terrifyingly strong jaws while Fox was hanging in midair on his way to the lamb. Buru caught Fox just inches away from gripping the lamb with his teeth.

The lamb jumped its small jump and moved a few feet away from where Fox was going to land and where Buru now stood. Fox cried in pain from Buru's strong bite. Fox knew that he could not escape Buru's dangerous jaws. Just as Buru caught Fox, an object came flying and hit Buru squarely in the face.

As Benin watched Buru move closer to the lamb, he was not going to let Buru get to the lamb first.

Benin had found a rock and decided to throw it toward Buru to scare Buru away from the lamb. As Benin was in the act of getting ready to throw the rock, he saw Fox leaping from the opposite side toward the lamb. Benin's throwing of the rock and Fox's leap happened almost at the same time. By the time the rock hit Buru, Buru had already grabbed Fox.

Both Buru and Fox were in pain. Buru let go of his bite as soon as the rock struck him in the face. Fox began hobbling away. Buru, surprised by the attack on him, moved back from where he stood. As Buru was evaluating his surroundings, Benin was finally close enough for Buru to see him. Injured and in pain, Buru retreated, and Benin collected his lamb and took it to its mother.

Benin, nearly having lost one of his animals, thought to himself that he needed to do a better job counting all his animals. Happy that he now had all his animals, and mother and child safely together again, he locked up his barn.

He checked the area for any possible dangerous animals again, but he did not see any. Then he went inside his home to rest for the night. Fox and Buru were still hungry and now injured, too. But the lamb slept comfortably under the watchful eyes of its mother.

THE END

Made in the USA
Middletown, DE
20 June 2025